This book is dedicated to my mom, dad and brother. To my niece and nephew.

To the sacred Waters.

To all the plants, creatures, and trees.

To my cousin Bobby and what he taught me - to his mother, father and brothers.

To my ancestors, teachers, and friends.

To my grandmother, who kept the spirit of magic and dreaming alive in me.

To how hard things can be.

To the spirit of love.

To tea.

TEA

Can we measure our lives in cups of tea? Tea with those who seem strange to us, with those who are beloved, or with those who come to us as both? Tea by the ocean, in the woods, on our front porch during a summer rain, in daylight and in the night, under the moon and in dreams? Or in our Grandmother's front room?

Can we measure our lives by the cups of quiet tea, medicine, offered and received in times of sadness or sickness. In the ways we've felt the distance, as well as the closeness, between us and everyone we've sat with longing to hear their truth, their story, their song?

Or by all the tea sipped in reverence of each other. The tea we raise to all the pain we've transformed into music, poetry, and beauty — into roaring laughter and our mischievous smiles when we knew, somehow, we were on the other side of it all.

May the distance between us all be healed by a smile and story told over a perfectly brewed cup of tea.

TEA WITH ME

If you and I sat down for tea, perhaps mint or rosemary, you might notice I'm blue. And if you ask me why, I'd say, "I'm a girl who thinks a lot about colors and the rainbow, too. But, blue is my favorite hue." Sometimes being blue means I don't have a face or an identity that is clear to you. Sometimes, being blue means I'm you, too.

If you and I had tea, I might ask you, "What if you and I have found where every sign leads to: right here, right now? Maybe all our destinies have already been fulfilled. Maybe we can just chill." And maybe we'd smile, clinking our spoons on the edge of our cups to spread the honey.

We'd watch the steam rising into the crisp morning air, and we'd forgive all the ways we tell ourselves we've failed. All the "wrong turns" we tell ourselves that if they were "right" we might have healed the lack we've always felt - the lack we've been taught to feel.

We'd look at each other and see what a miracle a person is. And we'd laugh and chat about the weather. "How wonderful it is to see you, here." I'd say.

And then, perhaps, I'd tell you about my Grandma, Bertha, and having tea in her front room when I was a young blue girl.

TEA WITH BERTHA

My grandmother on my mother's side, Bertha, was like a strange birch tree in a thick wood. Maybe you've seen a tree like this, one that stands out from the rest - A creature out of place. You know there's something to this tree, something ancient, something beautiful. You know this tree has a voice, it has stories.

She was tall, thin, beautiful — awkward but somehow graceful, too. She was like a creature you greet in a dream, like a mystery, wondering if she might sing songs made from eons of wise things.

But, so much of my Grandmother felt hidden. I suppose because a woman of her time had to know how to hide things. Sometimes she would play mischievously with veils, revealing - then hiding the light within - just so you would seek it out again. Winking as she turned around a dark corner, beckoning.

Every Sunday, I'd sit surrounded by the safe way she listened and loved me, that great orange light of comfort. Her dog at her feet. She taught me that dreams were more than they seemed, that life was more than it seemed, and to never discount the unseen things.

It has been many years since I sat with my grandma sipping tea…

Tea With An Artist

My mother once told me something that saved my life. She told me, "The things you fear the most have the most important things to teach you." She was an artist and she was right. I have loved plenty in this life, like tea, the sound of cicadas, and the Ocean. But, I have also spent a lot of time being afraid, afraid of people, strangers, war, men, hatred, stigma, illness, death...even Whales. But my mother's words turned me towards these frightening things so I could see what they had to teach me about myself and humanity. Not many understand the heart of creativity.

Not only did she tell me this, she also gave me the tools I needed to look deeply, transform, and share. She showed me how to see a frightening thing and learn from it by wrestling and representing it somehow in art, manipulating and transforming it in the context of art-making.

Growing up my mother and I, like her mother and I, sat together on many nights wrapped in orange with warm tea talking about what it meant to feel safe enough to do this, to make art, to face what we feared, to face the world, life, and to still see beauty everywhere, even in things many people think are ugly or broken.

TEA WITH THE RUNAWAY

Who is a person, a voice, disembodied by time and the trauma they left behind? The damage they did is like poison in a river, generations deep. The secrets and silences that are held, the blame some assume to protect what they loved the most - the future.

My father's mother was the runaway. Her abandonment was the loss my family lived over and over again.

One day I found a tape she had sent my brother and I when we were very young. She spent a few days recording herself talking about her days, what she did, the mocking bird she found and was helping to save, the laundry, and our cousins, the worn out tires on her son's car and government checks that weren't coming. Even some artwork she was making for us. She lived in Mississippi at the time.

In one story, about the mocking bird, she said the only difference between her and a mother bird was that she could not fly, and it struck me.

Who is this mother of my dad, this person who bled for my life, for his, yet, was the wound that nearly took it, too? Who is this person, a voice, disembodied by time and the trauma she left behind?

Grandma Jeanne

5:23   −24:54

TEA WITH A FREEMASON

Our family's surname was borrowed from an ancestor who's name had been lost in the tree. It was put on the birth certificate to avoid the stigma of my father having no father to name. So a slight misspelling of the Swedish name Jaevert, became Jervert.

My father said to me he knew this as a boy and decided he would make the name mean something. Now, Jervert means all the things he taught me and my brother. How painful it can be to live by a code of honor, by any code at all. How painful it can be to make a vow and believe in its eternity. But that is what being a Jervert meant to him. How to be a man, how to be a Freemason.

It was the way reality can be counted. How sometimes the unseen wasn't sturdy enough to rely on. The way a bridge is built by gravity, and the way a man can persevere through nearly anything. How the Ocean, when you need her is there. How in the toughest of skins, there is just wanting, a longing for mother.

I have always felt that underneath it all, Freemasons long for the Goddess, for the mother of things, just like my father always did. How we all do, watching the stars of the night sky, hoping we can make our lives mean something more.

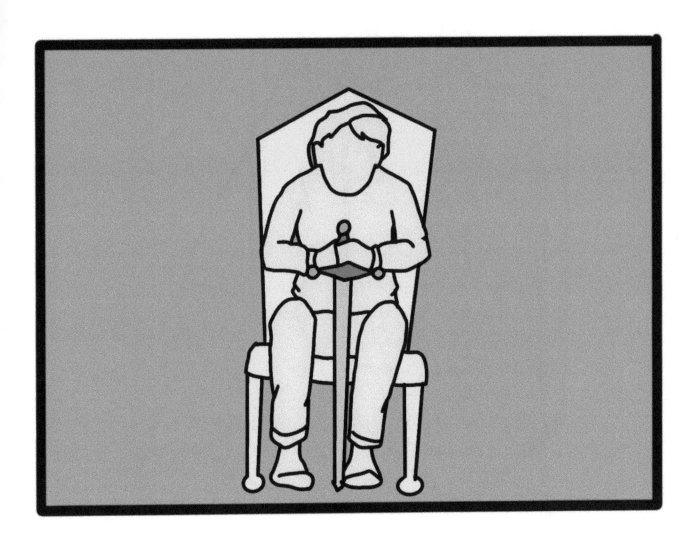

Have you ever glimpsed all of you? In all of time? And knew the only thing to do was surrender, lay your hands on the Earth & pray untill you meet your power, your love—The love that wears a crown.

Tea With a Zerker

In my 40s, I invited my brother, who is 4 years older than me, to a camping trip in the woods of Pennsylvania by the Susquehanna River.

I had begun my journey of coming off of psychiatric drugs a few years before. In my 20s I was labeled Bipolar. I was heading back to myself after almost 20 years of over medication and psychiatric abuse and trauma.

For a few years I had been doing ritual healing work around the Ocean, the Rivers, and the element of water itself. I'm not sure he understood the path I was taking around this kind of ritual, but that day by the water I looked at him playing on the rocks in the stream, a man now, and remembered what it was like to see him as a boy.

After I let go of an offering into the River that day, I looked on my brother again as I looked on him when I was a girl, with pride and envy. In this way I could sense his pain and courage and grace. How a part of me always wanted to be more like him. I remembered how much I looked up to him as he was learning the world, how he moved in it.

A lot had changed since that time in our lives. At night, by the camp fire, we talked about soul and the flower of life, and he said words that helped me on my journey.

TEA WITH EPONINE

When I was young, I used to wonder what love was besides wanting - wanting someone. Or wanting the poetry of the moonlight. And then I one day I was in love with a girl who sang a sad, lonely song under a street light. A girl who wanted what she knew she couldn't have. Who would give up her life for it still.

At 13, I remember wondering if someday I would do the same for love, for wanting.

I remember wondering if this wanting, my love, would ever find a home. When you're young and just growing into Queer love, sometimes you don't even know that that's what it is. But at that time, I didn't know then what might become of me or my love, no one ever does.

Especially not at 13 years old looking out a bedroom window, bathed in moonlight, reciting strange poems not even she understood. Wanting more than anything to sing them out loud one day. One day, the moon would speak and then...then would she be loved?

TEA WITH ANI DIFRANCO

When I noticed that the world had realized I was a woman, and all that seemed to come with it, there was this way I knew I was right to be filled with rage and hurt. I was so jealous of how my brother's body moved in the world, how in so many ways, he always had a way out, some way to be free of this gaze that seemed so threatening to me. Where he could stand firm, I felt I had to hide, to run. I knew enough about rage at 15 to die my hair bright orange and smoke pot and do LSD on a hill by a River in a park in a small 'hip' town in New Jersey. To walk the beach at 2am and get cigarettes from a vending machine at the laundry mat.

In the music of the folk/rock singer Ani Difranco I found my rage reflected back. She also inspired my desire to act on injustice. I remember quoting some lyrics of hers from "Not a Pretty Girl" when some girls teased me for how I tried to hide my body in the girls locker room with a trick my mother had taught me; how to take off my bra without taking off my shirt. And when she came out with her album with Utah Philips, a peace and labor activist and a story teller, the world of social injustices and learning to stand up for what you believe in became another way I channeled my rage around what it meant to be a woman in the world.

Tea With Tori Amos

In 2022, coming out of a global pandemic, I drove through town and watched water from a recent rain find its way from the oceans to the Rivers by way of the street gutters. Then suddenly, like a vision, I saw water everywhere. In the trees especially, but in the sky, too. Even in the people, in the birds, and the cars. When I think of it, it was like a flood, like the whole world was suddenly under sacred water, a kind of sacred lake. But I was not drowning - I was just floating there in beauty wondering how can anyone not see the water in how all things are made, how they are nurtured and how they grow?

I wonder the same thing about sound. Some musician's sound changes you forever, changes your life, your destiny even. This was Tori Amos for me. Her music was where my spiritual self resonated. She was a guide into the depth of my self, my emotions, and into another world, the underworld, the shadows of life.

It is beautiful how artists can change each other. Through her music and the resonance I found there, whether I knew it or not, a story emerged that I began to follow. In that sonic architecture a map was created. One I did not even know I was following...

Tea With Bobby

When my brother and I were young, my cousin and his family visited us every summer. I always looked for the old AMC Gremlin car they would park in my grandmother's driveway when they drove down from Ohio.

One summer, when Bobby was in his 20s, my mother commented on how strange it was that he was so excited to see his grandmother. Only now, do I think I know why. My grandmother believed in a world of unseen things. She believed in communication with the dead and dreams.

My cousin shot himself at an altar he had built in a shed surrounded by his sacred things. He was 21 years old. He was just a boy. I was 18. It was the year I graduated high school and got my first tattoo. It was the year I got arrested for possessing Marijuana, driving with seeds and stems in the glove box of my first car, an old 1980 Volvo.

It was the year I wrote my first suicide note, folded it up and pinned it to the cork board above the desk in my bedroom. It was the year a terrible, different kind of pain, was born inside me.

TEA WITH THE WOLF

For years leading up to my 20s, the loss, the loneliness and the pain of the ways life felt wild and cruel and disconnected from meaning was only just subdued under my surface. One summer day, just before transferring into Bard College, I sat outside by the Maple tree. In the Sun of things, I had a strange confidence, a sense of belonging, of place and purpose. My soul, like a Wolf, felt whole with me, connected in that profound moment with nature.

Later that night, I played a favorite Tori Amos song. I sat on the floor in front of the stereo transfixed by the eerie sound of it. I felt a strong calling to something powerful, some destiny unformed, undefined. When the song was over, I heard a beautiful sound coming from the stars, in the visionary world of my mind, and I didn't understand it then. There was so much I did not understand. I did not understand then that this moment would be the beginning of a struggle the force of which I could not have imagined.

I was starting to be in touch with a part of my mind, a part of this world, or another one, that would lead me to an unknown, very beautiful, and eventually very dangerous place.

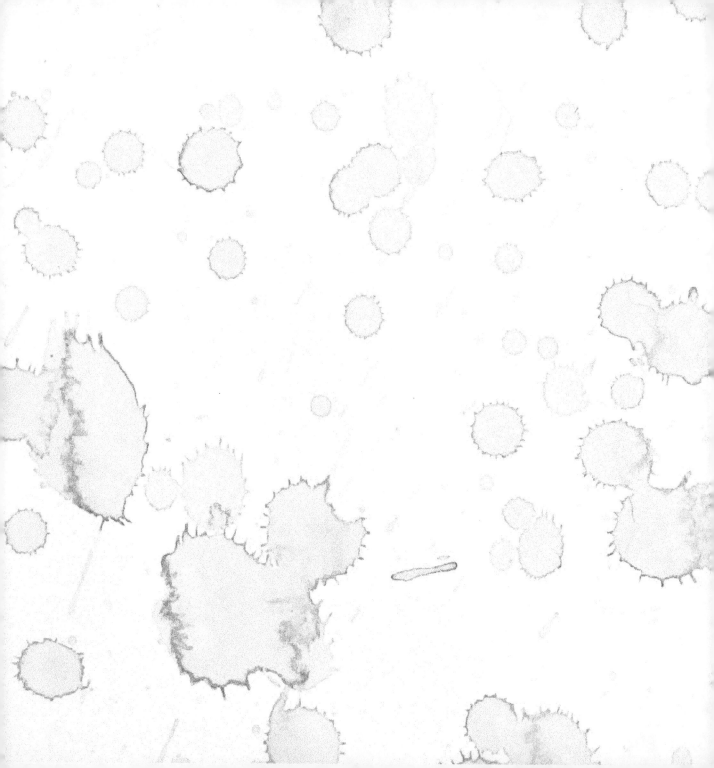

TEA WITH UNREQUITED LOVE

At school, I it didn't take me long to fall in love with a girl who wasn't in love with me. She was an energetic woman. Bulky, blonde, intelligent, compassionate, funny, yet rude and edgy. A New Yorker who would tell me not to mention I was from New Jersey, for the shame of it all.

She was kind to me. She was cool. She was calm. She studied math and a sculpture. She was the center of my world and she became a kind of Sophia or Beatrice to me, an inspiration. In my journal I wrote of a strange awakening of my senses:

> "Have I ever loved so much before? Could these fall breezes and sunlight, the laughter, could they have been here all along? Quick but soft and loyal – the cold through the window frame that looks at me, that breathes. The look of things. The battleground of my heart's passions and my hunger and my lust. The ground on which my feet stutter and my fingers stumble. Beauty. You. Even me sometimes, when I know nothing of myself, only everything of you."

Tea With A Moth and a Flame

One day, it sounded like people where banging on the walls of my room. And voices appeared in my mind, and time seemed to travel whichever way it chose.

And there I was in love with a girl who didn't love me, I was in love with autumn, writing poetry, and not knowing anything much about anything.

One day I lost the thread of things and no one had a story that could make sense of it for me. One day my mind filled with chaos and I had no idea what to say about it all.

One day nothing but the vividness of my mind mattered. The bright flame of it. And one day I walked out of my dorm room and the flowers were brighter than the Sun itself. Suddenly, I was a moth drawn to that flame, the brightness of everything, without knowing what dangers I drew to me.

One day I became a visionary, a seeker, a seer, a dreamer…

Tea with Another Me

I had always heard that spiritual stories always had a jokester, someone in the epic narrative of your life, or all of our lives, that had a mysterious and frustrating intention of creating confusion and calamity so you could see clearly. Be a mirror to your least admirable traits, to the worlds - a bird of pray, a coyote, a jester a joker - the joke itself.

But I never felt, with all the the world was, with the sorrow I felt in my bones, that there was a joke at the foundations, at the root. The joke was the playful ridicule of your smallness, your propensity for splitting into parts, of being confused as a being so sure of their grandeur.

The vividness of mind, the banging on the walls, that day the flowers shown like the Sun, split me in two, then in threes and fours. I was no longer one mind. I was many minds trying desperately to get home to unity. But, that is how epic stories are made, no? That is how all the stories start - a fracture and a desperate hope for home, for wholeness and healing.

I did find out who I was. In time I was able to rest as one, but it was long journey until then…

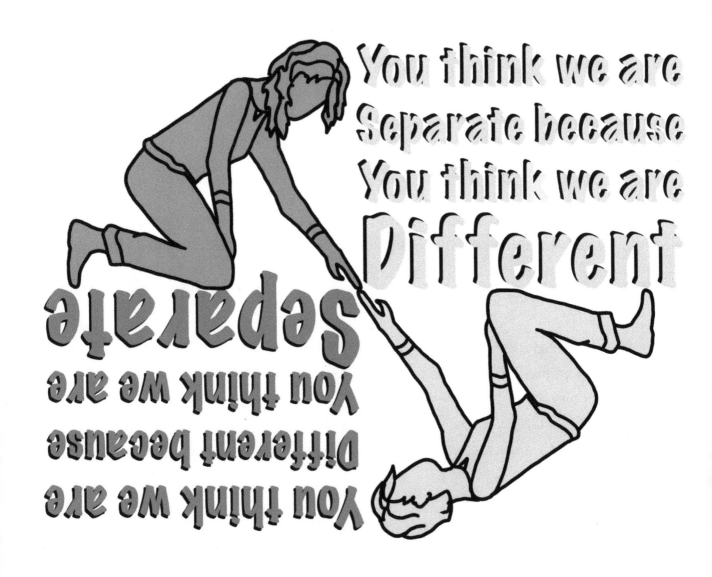

TEA AFTER THE WHITE FLAG

At this time in my life, I wish I had remembered that day by the Maple tree, I wish I had thought more about the trees. If a tree could have texted me, as a crippling aloneness crept over my life, it would have written me every morning as I woke, "I will support you all your life. Unfailingly. Don't forget that." If the soil of the Earth could have texted me, it would have written me every afternoon and it would have said, "I will hold you upright and provide for you as long as you live. Don't forget that." And if the sky could have texted me, it would at night as I lay down to sleep and it would have said, "I will never hold you back, I will never lie to you, I will show you the path." And every day I would have been filled with gratitude. Every day.

Sometimes the only choice to save what is precious feels like surrendering but we find out later was the biggest fight of our life. Sometimes facing the modern world, the stories we are told, the 'treatments' we receive for our confusion, our pain, are devastating. And sometimes knowing the damage done is so tender and so heartbreaking…

TEA IN A SOLITARY CELL

It's a long story to tell. It's a long story just to say, in my confusion, something horrible was done to me.

Something so dark that the walls of it still live in me. Sometimes the image of them still confines me there. So cold and hopeless, it became a darkness, a paralysis, I lived in for years and years and years. A void I threw things I hated into, a ripping apart of the fabric of my life into which I sank and sank and sank.

I was hospitalized in a mental hospital 4 times in my life. But, when I lost the thread of consensus reality, when I went 'mad' the day the towers fell in NYC, I was put in a solitary cell, with just a mattress. The walls were covered in small light green tiles, just one half underground window exposed the roots of a bush and a small bit of sky.

It took so many years, so many spirits, dreams, teachers and friends to break me free of it. Sacred water, places, people, and tea — lessons so painful, forces so powerful, all to show me that I had to fight back and then learn not to fight at all again. To show me how to be free, how to see differently. To show me again that I belonged, that I could move.

ROSEMARY TEA WITH DURGA

How do you teach someone that they are free despite what is done to them? Despite the prisons the world puts them in? How do you teach someone not to take the walls of a solitary cell in a mental institution personally? How not to take injury, war, death, violence, ignorance, chaos, darkness, being wrenched from the things we love, how not to take all that personally or accept the role of victim?

How does one live and love, and yet find themselves alone in the sovereignty of the the soul itself - the thing of light that hums in their breast? With Rosemary, Durga remembers the spark of your soul's flame, always.

"Against the door of death, I knew my power, but, I gave it away anyway…" I said to her.

Durga looked at me,

"Then Kali is the one who has the key to set you free."

Tea with the Dove's Gift

Kindness is a bird, a mourning dove, offered three times when you are sure you don't deserve what has been given.

Kindness is a gift of hope given despite any harm you have done yourself, or the learning still needed for you to love.

Kindness is a gift offered again and again with patience, kindness and a forgiveness that lives in all of us. Kindness is a path to forgive.

Some stories tell of those who offer love and mercy to even those who have tried to stole something precious from them, because they know it cannot be stolen.

The gifts given that we feel are not deserved are the sweetest of them all. Because of these kindnesses we can clearly see that there is nothing here to waste, nothing of us that is not enough.

And the kindness still comes, because it is what we're all made of.

Tea with a Biker Nun

A Buddhist nun once stood on the roof of a hospital, a nurse, a leather jacket wearing biker, and said to herself, "there has to be more to this life than just this!" Next thing, she found herself in the desert somewhere in the 1960s screaming into the void of things, the void of herself and hearing a voice say back, "Have you had enough, yet?"

The universe - Have you had enough of yourself now, love? And she crawled into the robes of a nun and taught me one day many years later to shut the hell up in my head. To listen to when it's all too much. To stop the static from fraying everything precious. Not to let the heat of the confusion burn away the compassion it takes to be whole, healed. To be kind. To love. To be of service.

To care for the Water that servers us, and to learn to use my gifts to serve kindness. "Out of Service, Jervert" she once said to me after I read a poem to a group of meditators. A flash of inspiration - out of service she reminded me, quickly, not to miss the moment of a perfect teaching there that day. These gifts are here for you and for me to learn to serve. Pointing it out perfectly.

Tea with Kali

When it seems there's nothing more, Kali makes you drink your fire and stand up.

> "You must learn to drink your fire, my love," She said.

> "The fire of fault, of rage, and blame.

> The fire of shame.

> Of remembering the choices you made.

> The things you gave away..."

Here is the story of how from that day on, from that darkness, I grew and grew, until all I had left was the medicine I needed to heal, create a new life, and be whole again.

TEN THOUSAND THINGS

In the halls of psychiatry, I was told to fear, ignore and try to eradicate all the things going on inside me, the things I saw and heard and felt. All ten thousand things.

In Buddhist philosophy, the "Ten thousands things" is a way of saying "everything," or "all dharmas," or truths. In Taoism, the name (meaning the name of a thing) is the mother of ten thousand things — Like in the bible, as God spoke to create the universe. In Egyptian mythology, the Goddess Isis had ten thousand names.

In ancient times, ten thousand was a number that encompassed all manifestations of the universe as one. The ten thousand things can also refer to boundless creativity, to diversity as the foundation of nature. But, somehow 'everything' has become only 'some things' these days. Some people, some thoughts, some experiences, some skin colors, some genders, some income brackets, some philosophies, some religions. There are those who think only some things should be a part of the whole thing - all of existence.

But, Nature's most profound and fundamental mechanism for life is diversity. And seeking life, balance, and harmony, nature always wins.

TEA WITH PERSEPHONE

As I'm dragged into the underworld to face the dark Sea of pain that was my life after three hospitalizations, what my futile pleas must sounded like to the ears of a universe as if it was listening to itself deny its own nature.

As it plots its way forward only as it does - confused by the sound, with no memory of any intention of good or evil.

"What is this pitiful begging? This sound, so saturated with sorrow?"

It is only me, a woman stolen from spring, stolen from youth, casting her fears towards the sun as I'm gripped by the underworld, that shadow of things.

And the sun? The Sun that will do nothing to save me from falling deeper into the dark.

What must Persephone's song sound like to ears like these? As she begs to remain in the realm of life, as the Earth - lazily, arbitrarily, and without care for her loss - spins, as it does, away from the light into night?

TEA WITH DEMETER

I have always found silence the hardest thing. I would rather weep, in song, in poetry. But, my mother, as she felt the grief of losing me in 'madness', in a broken system of health care, to addiction and a paralyzed consciousness, she learned the silences she had to keep.

I know she wept in her own house, but with me, she kept strong and even angry. Pressing parts of me to check the flesh for life, to check that I could smile still.

There was a time after the mental hospital, a year or more, where I didn't smile at all. One day a joke was made and I finally smiled.

With mothers I think there are two kinds of joy, and one kind of rage. One kind of joy is to see the pain slip away, another kind are the tears of loving the life you made with all your hopes and dreams, with all your confusion and theories about why you were made, too. Here's that life you made smiling again, after years of a stone face. After so much pain.

Then there is the scorched Earth of a mother's rage. The revenge of Demeter, and the determination of spring to rise again…

Tea With My Beloved Dead

There was a poem on my grandmother's bedroom wall she kept that I had written, at the end of my rope, in such a dark place, when she passed. It said,

"When the Earth disappears, Your attachment to it will slip away sweetly, As if you were eating a sweet fruit.

I will not beg you to stay—I will sing you a lullaby, As if this was not goodbye forever, Only goodbye for now.

You will never again be the cause. You will never again be the solution. You will not be inconsolable, For I will console you.

The earth will disappear. With everyone in it all at once. Dreams gone, desires gone, fear gone, death gone."

What a strange way death can be such a teacher. What a strange way those we love, in their death, can hold a prayer for us, for life - so we might hold onto something precious no matter what.

These days grandma & I meet only in dreams...

We have tea together under a white sky & a black moon, & she reminds me to be careful with precious things.

TEA ON MY OWN AGAIN

When I stepped into the world again after all I had experienced, I was left with nothing much to understand it, to make meaning out of what had happened to me, or what might happen to me. Not much to make sense of death or pain or love and joy, I was left with a kind of skeletal architecture of Christianity and the disease model of my brain.

What immense divinities get lost in our desperate rationalities. I lived on my own, and struggled to understand myself and my world, but I was lost. I had no sense of meaning or soul or spirituality. I was over medicated, I smoked a ton of pot, I drank, I was isolated and in so much pain for so long.

I had moved out of my parents house in 2005, and struggled terribly, but after my grandmother passed, I struggled even more to keep my independence. My mom would visit and we would talk like we had when I was I was a kid at home, or with Grandma, curled up with tea on the couch.

Besides one or two other friends, she and my art practice were my only connections to the world, I had lost a sense of belonging here…

Tea Alone

Years after her passing, I found a dream my grandmother had written on a grocery store receipt. She warned or quipped, don't pay attention to your dreams. Even if she had practiced Tarot and believed in all those sacred, unseen, things, she was always afraid of the way Bobby died...and so was I, so was my whole family.

Then one day in March 2020, the COVID19 Pandemic hit and I learned how to be alone. I started coming off psychiatric medication. And then I started to dream again. I started to think there was something more to life than just one reality of things. One night I dreamt a wolf that leapt into my chest. It was so real. Perhaps after all these years, I thought, my soul had returned to me.

Engaging in spirituality was terrifying. But music, dreams, and my growing curiosity about my diversities of mind, the voices and visions I experienced, was slowly replacing the fear nurtured by psychiatry. And I was drawn closer to the power of magic, and nature, and poetry as a way to make sense of the confusion and to heal, to reclaim my belonging. The world gave me no clues except that I had a disease and that was the end of my story. But I started to realize there was more...that maybe that was never true.

Tea for Spirit

One night, I dreamt of mint tea and remembered the comfort of siting with my grandmother in her front room. I had been exploring more and more the diversities of my mind, the power of nature, and facing my deepest fears. Fears I had developed over years of being told what was right and what was wrong about the way I felt, the way I thought, the way I perceived.

It seemed more and more my journey was becoming one where over time I was releasing all my fears. And when I decided to sit at an old Buddhist altar I had made years before as I learned to meditate, and offer the gift of a warm cup of tea there - I started to realize the path of gratitude and offerings, of ritual and story.

I sat down with the Mystery that day, and began a practice of doing this every day. Over time my altar grew and grew, the stories that were told laid threads here and there in my life to follow, and all my fears fell away one at a time. Not that it was easy…I held Bobby in mind and hoped I could be an example of how it might have been to thrive in the unseen world of spirit.

And then I began having tea with all sorts of things.

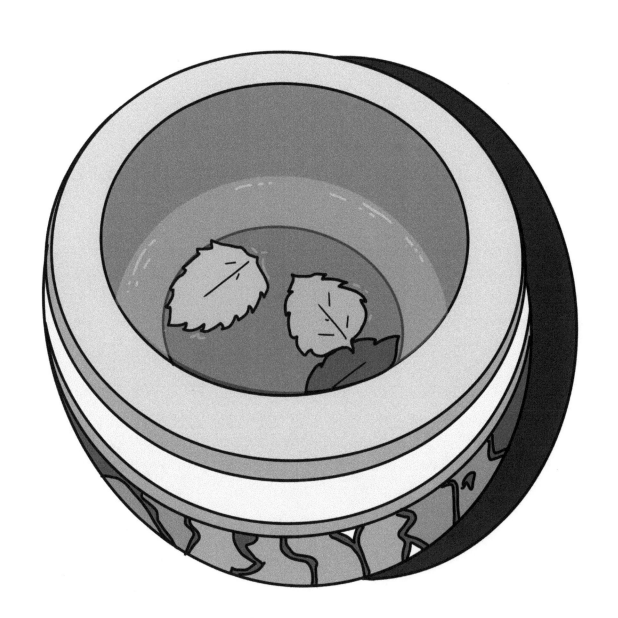

Tea with the Woman in the Stars

I asked the Woman in the Stars to tell me where she was from, what it was like when she was young. She showed me her story in the stars. I had heard their song before, those notes from so far off, so far into the dark.

How could I have understood the pain behind those sounds in the night sky? Or what it all actually meant, listening on the wrong side of the veil? By her fire, I feel sad and sorry that, even still…even still…all these years on…I don't understand. Wondering, am I betrayed by everyone? Is there no one? No one at all who can tell me the truth of you? Of me?

There's nothing else for her to do, she says. She has told me her story, sung all the songs, she's done her part. Just like the others. She listened to the voices of the living and of the dead - and I am happy for her - a life well lived. I sip my tea silently. If only I could join her there. Among those beautiful warriors. But, if her and I are done, the songs still find their way home to me - who knows why. And I am listening, alone, ignorant, and exhausted.

A Prayer for the Spiritual Education of the Dead

I sit down each morning at my altar filled with sacred things and I bow to my cousin Bobby as the spiritual boy he was. I try remember, a life like this, a mind like this, a soul that twists like this, that sees like this, is possible. A spiritual life is possible.

I grieve that it was not that way in his life, and is still not that way for so many. I mourn him. And I mourn the girl I was in that solitary cell.

Let us learn to be guides through the possibilities of mind, through the Dark Woods of consciousness, the confusing paths we all walk. Let us find the travelers of the world, like my cousin, and sit with them with tea, surrounded by sacred things and show them the way, telling them our stories of hope and healing.

How the dark can become light again.

TEA WITH A DEER CAT

How does a dream become a drawing?

When I was a kid, I used to draw my dreams, but for many years, I entirely forgot that I had done this until I one day I started drawing my dreams again in my 40s.

Sometimes a bright image will appear in a series of images, like a story. Sometimes an image would appear alone. Those are the images easiest to draw because they are so clear and crisp. I wake up knowing just how it will look on the page…mostly, until I sit down with the pencil and I'm met with the limitations of reality and my skill.

The Deer Cat was the first dream character who came to me with tea, the inspiration for this book entirely. After he came, I thought what a great idea! And then others would come to have tea with me, in dreams, in visions, and in my imagination.

The concept grew and grew, and I knew some day it would become a book, a story of tea and 10,000 things.

TEA WITH DIFFERENCE

Sometimes a creature, a person, a thing, a feeling, an experience, a thought or behavior can feel so different that the fear of it creates a mythic anxiety, and draws us away from the truth of now, or what's important in any moment. Compassion.

There is so much about this world I don't understand, there is just as much that I don't understand about myself. The ways my mind works, the ways my body works, and hurts, and does what it does. The way light and sound, and love and sorrow, and pain and joy operate.

But, as I've learned, and something I try so hard to keep hold of as I am faced with difference after difference, is that light divided in 10,000 ways in 10,000 galaxies, is still kindness in the end. It is taking the risk of trusting, of talking, of being the one to reach out your hand. The emptiness of mind it takes to travel lightyears inward instead to find the courage that has us choosing kindness again and again?

It is a journey of enormous lengths, asked of us in seconds at a time. Day by day, breath by breath. In this universe and in the one next door.

TEA WITH A WHALE

Most of my life I was terrified of Whales.

I would have dreams of electric Whales, ones that stared at me, ones beached on the shore of some subconscious river flowing through memories of my of my childhood, and I was always afraid to look at them, into their eyes.

Their bodies were enormous, their intentions unknown, how they took up so much space in the vast sea. In one dream I was treading water in the middle of an endless ocean, and there they were circling beneath me.

One night I decided I would face the Whale and whatever it meant to me, and as I fell asleep I met a whale, and it grew and grew and grew, and then with my heart pounding, I decided that as it got bigger so would I, I would grow to be as big as it was so we could speak as equals.

We spoke and then I knew the intention of the whale was a benevolence, a kind of kindness and wisdom I had never felt before. And I was no longer afraid. In fact now I considered Whales to be close friends and guides. I even have a tattoo of one on my chest.

Some nights I imagine talking with them, asking them questions about life…

Tea with Friends

I spent a lot of time Isolated as an adult. Madness becomes a similar journey as it can be for chronic illness, disability, aging, and any difference. It's a deep aloneness that compounds and unfolds over time because of the stigma and fear around it.

I was very sick physically for a long time after COVID19 hit, too. I was withdrawing from 5 psychiatric medications, and then I was struck by chronic dizziness, fatigue, nausea, weakness and pain. But, I found comfort in friends, in peers in the Mad Pride movement, and in the Psychiatric Survivor movement.

Although it was still very lonely, living alone through all of this, people came to help me in all sorts of ways, different abilities plugged different holes in how I could care for myself, different friends held different shields that locked together to support me through what was one of the hardest times of my entire life. Some close friends I lost during this period, because they couldn't hold what I was going through, but so many stuck around. And after almost 3 years of illness, my body and my mind started to heal and find balance again…slowly.

SHIELD WALL!

TEA WITH MY ANCESTORS

As I healed from the effects of psychiatric trauma and over medication, I learned to embrace the ways I saw the world, unique as they were, I started to see it all as having roots in my cultural past, too.

I became curious about my family's history and found that on both sides I had Norse roots, going back quite a bit. Of course, my 'roots' do not end or begin there...I often think that how we perceive time and history and 'family' is sometimes so short sighted - generating so much territorialism and violence around who is who and what that means. But, the roles of women 'seers' in Norse culture stood out to me. Called the Völur, just like seers in many ancient cultures, these women had a unique way of seeing the world, just like me. And they served their communities, were valued, and were sought after for help and healing. They were medicine women, they were part of the fabric of things.

As a woman who had been deemed 'mad', who would otherwise spend the rest of her life anxiously awaiting the next incarceration in a hospital, the idea that I could be worth more, that this 'curse' could be a gift, too, opened the door wide to even deeper healing...

TEA WITH ME

If I had tea with me today, I would sit with a Wolf and a 20 year old slender thing sitting in the sun of a summer day, swept away by the power of existence, the force of light and nature and love. I'd sit with a girl under a beautiful Maple tree. Her soul filled with loyalty and love, and grit and determination, curiosity and creativity, I'd say, "damn, girl, look what you did. You made it through all of this. Here you are looking through your eyes again. Here you are able to see like you were meant to see."

I would never tell her what was coming next. One thing I know is that the future is an unnecessary burden. The lessons we learned, all the things we do, the lefts and the rights we take, and the shadows and pain - it's all ours to do with what we will. Her and I, we chose to have faith in the magic of things. Have faith in the sacred Water and the medicine of the Earth and of tea, the friendship of Wolves and Whales. The divinity of difference and how to tell a story creatively.

"The day the Wolf came back to me," I'd tell her, "I think I knew then that we would make it. And here we are," I'd say. "And, look at you." She'd smile and say, "Look at you."

www.ingramcontent.com/pod-product-compliance
Lightning Source LLC
LaVergne TN
LVHW061302201224
799582LV00018B/408